ArtNotes

to accompany

A Basic History of Art

SIXTH EDITION

H. W. Janson
Anthony F. Janson

Prentice
Hall

Upper Saddle River, New Jersey 07458

ISBN 0-13-184759-7

Printed in the United States of America

Museum credits for fine art photos can be found with the images in the text. Images in the supplement were supplied by SuperStock, Inc. Please note that where we have included artwork in ArtNotes, we have made every effort to secure the same photograph of the art that is found in your text. There are some instances, however, where we had to substitute a slightly different photograph of an object. Please consult your textbook if you are studying the objects for identification purposes.

Contents

Introduction

1. *Harpist,* so-called *Orpheus,* from Amorgos in the Cyclades. Latter part of the 3rd millennium B.C. *(page 17)*

2. Pablo Picasso. *Bull's Head.* 1943. *(page 18)*

3. Michelangelo. *Awakening Slave* (foreground). 1506. *(page 20)*

4. Michelangelo. Study for the *Libyan Sibyl.* c. 1511. *(page 23)*

5. Michelangelo. *Libyan Sibyl,* detail of the Sistine Ceiling. 1508–12. *(page 24)*

6. Titian. *Venus with a Mirror.* c. 1555.
(page 25)

7. Pablo Picasso. *Girl before a Mirror.* 1932.
(page 26)

8. Caravaggio. *David with the Head of Goliath.*
1607 or 1609/10. *(page 27)*

9. Jean-Baptiste-Siméon Chardin. *Blowing Bubbles.* c. 1745. *(page 27)*

10. El Greco. *The Agony in the Garden.* 1597–1600. *(page 28)*

11. *Hermes Leading Iphigeneia to Hades.* Lower column drum from the Temple of Artemis, Ephesus. c. 340 B.C. *(page 29)*

12. Praxiteles (attributed to). *Standing Youth,*
found in the sea off Marathon. c. 350–325 B.C.
(page 29)

13. Frank Lloyd Wright. Solomon R. Guggenheim
Museum, New York. 1956–59 *(page 30)*

14. Interior, Solomon R. Guggenheim Museum
(page 30)

15. Jan Vermeer. *Woman Holding a Balance.*
c. 1664. *(page 32)*

16. Jasper Johns. *Target with Four Faces.* 1955.
(page 33)

Chapter 1
Prehistoric Art in Europe and North America

Notes

1-1. Cave paintings, Chauvet cave, Vallon-Pont-d'Arc, Ardèche gorge, France. c. 28,000 B.C. *(page 41)*

_____

_____

_____

_____

_____

_____

_____

_____

_____

_____

1-2. Cave paintings, Lascaux, Dordogne, France. c. 15,000–10,000 B.C. *(page 41)*

_____

_____

_____

_____

_____

_____

_____

_____

_____

_____

_____

1-3. *Woman of Willendorf,* from Austria.
c. 25,000–20,000 B.C. *(page 43)*

1-4. *Woman,* from Hluboké Masuvky, Moravia,
Czech Republic. c. 3,000 B.C. *(page 43)*

1-5. Stonehenge, Salisbury Plain, Wiltshire,
England. c. 2000 B.C. *(page 44)*

1-6. Diagram of original arrangement of stones at Stonehenge (after original drawing by Richard Tobias) *(page 44)*

_____

_____

_____

_____

_____

_____

_____

_____

_____

_____

_____

1-7. Great Serpent Mound, Adams County, Ohio. c. 1070 A.D. *(page 46)*

_____

_____

_____

_____

_____

_____

_____

_____

_____

_____

_____

Chapter 2
Egyptian Art

2-1, 2-2. *Palette of King Narmer* (both sides), from Hierakonpolis. c. 3150–3125 B.C. *(page 49)*

_____

_____

_____

_____

_____

_____

_____

_____

_____

_____

_____

2-3. *Ti Watching a Hippopotamus Hunt*, Tomb of Ti, Saqqara. c. 2510–2460 B.C. *(page 51)*

_____

_____

_____

_____

_____

_____

_____

_____

_____

_____

2-4. *Menkaure and His Wife, Queen Khamerernebty,*
from Giza. c. 2515 B.C. *(page 52)*

2-5. Imhotep. Step pyramid of King Djoser,
Saqqara. c. 2681–2662 B.C. *(page 54)*

2-6. Papyrus half-columns, North Palace, funerary
district of King Djoser, Saqqara *(page 54)*

2-7. The Pyramids of Menkaure (c. 2533–2515 B.C.), Khafre (c. 2570–2544 B.C.), and Khufu (c. 2601–2528 B.C.), Giza *(page 55)*

2-8. Plan of necropolis at Giza with sections of Pyramid of Khufu and mastaba, and with inset of step pyramid of King Djoser at Saqqara *(page 56)*

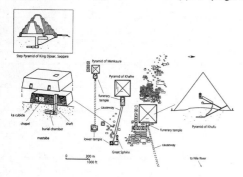

2-9. The Great Sphinx, Giza. c. 2570–2544 B.C. *(page 57)*

2-10. *Feeding the Oryxes.* Modern copy of an original at the Tomb of Khnumhotep, Beni Hasan. c. 1928–1895 B.C. *(page 58)*

2-11. Temple of Queen Hatshepsut, Deir el-Bahri. c. 1478–1458 B.C. *(page 59)*

2-12. *Akhenaten and His Family.* c. 1355 B.C. *(page 60)*

2-13. *Queen Nefertiti.* c. 1348–1336/5 B.C. *(page 61)*

2-14. Cover of the coffin of Tutankhamun. c. 1327 B.C. *(page 62)*

2-15. Court and pylon of Ramesses II and colonnade and court of Amenhotep III, Temple of Amun-Mut-Khonsu, Luxor. c. 1279–1212 B.C. *(page 63)*

Chapter 3
Ancient Near Eastern Art

Notes

3-1. Remains of the "White Temple" on its zig-gurat, Uruk (Warka), Iraq. c. 3500–3000 B.C.
(page 66)

_____

_____

_____

_____

_____

_____

_____

_____

_____

_____

_____

3-2. Plan of the "White Temple" (after H. Frankfort)
(page 66)

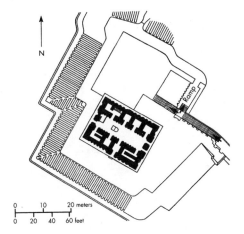

_____

_____

_____

_____

_____

_____

_____

_____

_____

_____

3-3. Statues, from the Abu Temple, Tell Asmar,
Iraq. c. 2700–2500 B.C. *(page 67)*

3-4. *Ram and Tree.* Offering stand from Ur
(Muqaiyir), Iraq. c. 2600 B.C. *(page 68)*

3-5. Inlay panel from the soundbox of a harp,
from Ur (Muqaiyir), Iraq. c. 2600 B.C. *(page 69)*

3-6. *Gudea*, from Lagash (Telloh), Iraq. c. 2120 B.C. *(page 69)*

3-7. Upper part of stela inscribed with the Law Code of Hammurabi, from Susa (Shush), Iran. c. 1760 B.C. *(page 71)*

3-8. *Ashurnasirpal II Killing Lions*, from the Palace of Ashurnasirpal II, Calah (Nimrud), Iraq. c. 850 B.C. *(page 72)*

3-9. Ishtar Gate (restored), from Babylon, Iraq.
c. 575 B.C. *(page 73)*

3-10. Fragment of a belt, probably from
Ziwiye. 7th century B.C. *(page 73)*

3-11. Audience Hall of Darius and Xerxes,
Persepolis, Iran. c. 500 B.C. *(page 75)*

Chapter 4
Aegean Art

Notes

4-1. Figure, from Amorgos, Cyclades. c. 2500 B.C. *(page 77)*

_____

_____

_____

_____

_____

_____

_____

_____

_____

_____

_____

4-2. The Queen's Megaron, Palace of Minos, Knossos, Crete. c. 1700–1300 B.C. *(page 79)*

_____

_____

_____

_____

_____

_____

_____

_____

_____

_____

4-3. *"Snake Goddess,"* from the palace complex, Knossos. c. 1650 B.C. *(page 80)*

4-4. *"The Toreador Fresco,"* from the palace complex, Knossos. Original c. 1500 B.C.; restored. *(page 81)*

4-5. Interior, "Treasury of Atreus," Mycenae. c. 1300–1250 B.C. *(page 82)*

4-6. The Lioness Gate, Mycenae. 1250 B.C.
(page 83)

Chapter 5
Greek Art

5-1. *Dipylon Vase,* from the Dipylon cemetery, Athens. 8th century B.C. *(page 86)*

_____

_____

_____

_____

_____

_____

_____

_____

_____

_____

_____

5-2. *The Blinding of Polyphemos and Gorgons,* on a Proto-Attic amphora. c. 675–650 B.C. *(page 88)*

_____

_____

_____

_____

_____

_____

_____

_____

_____

_____

5-3. Psiax. *Herakles Strangling the Nemean Lion*, on an Attic black-figured amphora from Vulci, Italy. c. 525 B.C. *(page 91)*

5-4. Euphronios. *Herakles Wrestling Antaios*, on an Attic red-figured krater. c. 510 B.C. *(page 92)*

5-5. *The Battle of Issos* or *The Battle of Alexander and the Persians*. c. 100 B.C. *(page 93)*

5-6. Ground plan of a typical Greek peripteral temple *(page 95)*

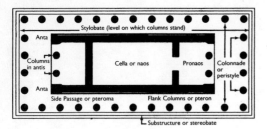

5-7. Doric order *(page 96)*

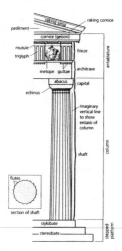

5-8. The Temple of Hera I, c. 550 B.C., and the Temple of Hera II, c. 460 B.C., Paestum, Italy *(page 98)*

5-9. Iktinos, Kallikrates, and Karpion. The Parthenon (view of the west facade), Akropolis, Athens. 448–432 B.C. *(page 99)*

5-10. Mnesikles. The Propylaia, 437–432 B.C. (left and center), with the Temple of Athena Nike, 427–424 B.C. (right); Akropolis (view from the west), Athens *(page 101)*

5-11. *Kouros (Standing Youth).* c. 600 B.C. *(page 102)*

5-12. *Kore in Dorian Peplos.* c. 530 B.C. *(page 103)*

5-13. *Battle of the Gods and Giants,* from the
north frieze of the Treasury of the Siphnians,
Delphi. c. 530 B.C. *(page 104)*

5-14. *Dying Warrior,* from the east pediment
of the Temple of Aphaia, Aegina. c. 490 B.C.
(page 105)

5-15. *Kritios Boy.* c. 480 B.C. *(page 106)*

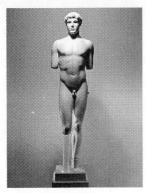

5-16. *Zeus.* c. 460–450 B.C. *(page 107)*

5-17. *Doryphoros (Spear Bearer).* Roman copy after an original of c. 450–440 B.C. by Polykleitos. *(page 108)*

5-18. *Battle of the Lapiths and Centaurs,* from the west pediment of the Temple of Zeus, Olympia. c. 460 B.C. *(page 109)*

_____

_____

_____

_____

_____

_____

_____

_____

_____

_____

_____

_____

5-19. *Dying Niobid.* c. 450–440 B.C. *(page 111)*

_____

_____

_____

_____

_____

_____

_____

_____

_____

_____

_____

_____

5-20. *Three Goddesses,* from the east pediment of the Parthenon. c. 438–432 B.C. *(page 112)*

_____

_____

_____

_____

_____

_____

_____

_____

_____

5-21. Skopas (?). *Battle of the Greeks and Amazons,* from the east frieze of the Mausoleum, Halikarnassos. 359–351 B.C. *(page 114)*

5-22. *Knidian Aphrodite.* Roman copy after an original of c. 340–330 B.C. by Praxiteles. *(page 114)*

5-23. Epigonos of Pergamon (?). *Dying Trumpeter.* Roman copy after a bronze original of c. 230–220 B.C., from Pergamon, Turkey. *(page 115)*

5-24. *Athena and Alkyoneos*, from the east
side of the Great Frieze of the Great Pergamon
Altar. c. 180 B.C. *(page 116)*

5-25. Pythokritos of Rhodes (?). *Nike of
Samothrace.* c. 190 B.C. *(page 117)*

5-26. Portrait head, from Delos. c. 80 B.C.
(page 117)

Chapter 6
Etruscan Art

Notes

6-1. Sarcophagus, from Cerveteri. c. 520 B.C. *(page 119)*

6-2. Tomb of Hunting and Fishing, Tarquinia, Italy. c. 520 B.C. *(page 121)*

6-3. *Youth and Demon of Death*. Cinerary container. Early 4th century B.C. *(page 122)*

_____

_____

_____

_____

_____

_____

_____

_____

_____

_____

_____

6-4. Reconstruction of an Etruscan temple. Museo delle Antichità Etrusche e Italiche, Rome *(page 122)*

_____

_____

_____

_____

_____

_____

_____

_____

_____

_____

_____

_____

6-5. *Apollo*, from Veii. c. 510 B.C. *(page 123)*

_____

_____

_____

_____

_____

_____

_____

_____

_____

_____

_____

_____

Notes

6-6. *She-Wolf.* c. 500 B.C. *(page 124)*

_____

_____

_____

_____

_____

_____

_____

_____

_____

_____

_____

_____

Chapter 7
Roman Art

Notes

7-1. Sanctuary of Fortuna Primigenia, Praeneste (Palestrina). Early 1st century B.C. *(page 127)*

_____
_____
_____
_____
_____
_____
_____
_____
_____
_____
_____

7-2. The Colosseum, Rome. 72–80 A.D. *(page 128)*

_____
_____
_____
_____
_____
_____
_____
_____
_____
_____
_____

7-3. The Pantheon, Rome. 118–25 A.D. *(page 129)*

7-4. Giovanni Paolo Pannini. *The Interior of the Pantheon.* c. 1740. *(page 130)*

7-5. Section of the Pantheon *(page 130)*

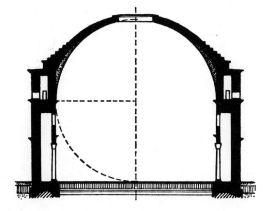

7-6. The Basilica of Constantine, Rome. c. 307–20 A.D.
(page 131)

7-7. Reconstruction drawing of the Basilica of
Constantine (after Huelsen) *(page 131)*

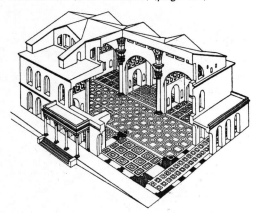

7-8. *A Roman Patrician with Busts of His
Ancestors.* Late 1st century B.C. *(page 132)*

7-9. *Augustus of Primaporta.* c. 20 A.D. Roman copy of a Roman original of c. 15 B.C. *(page 133)*

7-10. *Equestrian Statue of Marcus Aurelius.* 161–80 A.D. *(page 134)*

7-11. *Faustina the Younger.* c. 147–48 A.D. *(page 135)*

7-12. *Philippus the Arab.* 244–49 A.D. *(page 135)*

7-13. *Constantine the Great.* Early 4th century A.D. *(page 136)*

7-14. *Spoils from the Temple in Jerusalem.* Relief in passageway, Arch of Titus, Rome. 81 A.D. *(page 137)*

7-15. Lower portion of the Column of Trajan, Rome. 106–13 A.D. *(page 138)*

7-16. *The Laestrygonians Hurling Rocks at the Fleet of Odysseus*. Wall painting from the Odyssey Landscapes series in a house on the Esquiline Hill, Rome. Late 1st century B.C. *(page 140)*

7-17. *Scenes of a Dionysiac Mystery cult*. Mural frieze. c. 50 B.C. *(page 140)*

7-18. The Ixion Room, House of the Vettii,
Pompeii. 63–79 A.D. *(page 141)*

_____

_____

_____

_____

_____

_____

_____

_____

_____

_____

_____

_____

7-19. *Portrait of a Boy,* from the Faiyum,
Lower Egypt. 2nd century A.D. *(page 143)*

_____

_____

_____

_____

_____

_____

_____

_____

_____

_____

_____

_____

Chapter 8
Early Christian and Byzantine Art

Notes

8-1. Painted ceiling, Catacomb of SS. Pietro e Marcellino, Rome. 4th century *(page 154)*

8-2. S. Apollinare in Classe, near Ravenna. 533–49 *(page 157)*

8-3. Interior (view toward the apse), S. Apollinare in Classe *(page 157)*

8-4. *The Parting of Lot and Abraham*. Mosaic in Sta. Maria Maggiore, Rome. c. 432–40 *(page 159)*

8-5. Page with *Jacob Wrestling the Angel*, from the *Vienna Genesis*. Early 6th century. *(page 161)*

8-6. *Sarcophagus of Junius Bassus.* c. 359.
(page 163)

8-7. S. Vitale, Ravenna. 526–47 *(page 166)*

8-8. Interior (view from the apse), S. Vitale
(page 166)

8-9. *Emperor Justinian and His Attendants.*
Mosaic in S. Vitale. c. 547 *(page 168)*

8-10. *Empress Theodora and Her Attendants.*
Mosaic in S. Vitale. c. 547 *(page 168)*

8-11. Anthemius of Tralles and Isidorus of Miletus.
Hagia Sophia, Istanbul. 532–37 *(page 169)*

8-12. Interior, Hagia Sophia *(page 170)*

_____

_____

_____

_____

_____

_____

_____

_____

_____

_____

_____

8-13. *Madonna and Child Enthroned between Saints and Angels.* Late 6th century. *(page 172)*

_____

_____

_____

_____

_____

_____

_____

_____

_____

_____

_____

8-14. *The Archangel Michael.* Leaf of a diptych. c. 525–50. *(page 173)*

_____

_____

_____

_____

_____

_____

_____

_____

_____

_____

_____

8-15. *Nativity.* c. 1030–40. *(page 175)*

8-16. *Crucifixion.* Mosaic in Monastery Church, Daphne, Greece. Early 12th century *(page 175)*

8-17. *Lamentation.* Fresco in the Church of St. Panteleimon, Nerezi, Republic of Macedonia. 1164 *(page 176)*

8-18. *Madonna Enthroned.* Late 13th century.
(page 177)

_____

_____

_____

_____

_____

_____

_____

_____

_____

_____

_____

_____

8-19. *Anastasis.* Fresco in Kariye Camii (Church
of the Savior in Chora), Istanbul. c. 1310–20
(page 179)

_____

_____

_____

_____

_____

_____

_____

_____

_____

_____

_____

Chapter 9
Early Medieval Art

9-1. Purse cover, from the Sutton Hoo ship burial. 625–33. *(page 181)*

_____

_____

_____

_____

_____

_____

_____

_____

_____

_____

9-2. Animal head, from the Oseberg ship burial. c. 825. *(page 182)*

_____

_____

_____

_____

_____

_____

_____

_____

_____

_____

9-3. Cross page from the *Lindisfarne Gospels.*
c. 700. *(page 184)*

9-4. *Crucifixion.* Plaque from a book cover (?).
8th century. *(page 185)*

9-5. Odo of Metz. Interior, Palace Chapel of
Charlemagne, Aachen. 792–805 *(page 186)*

9-6. Façade, Abbey Church, Corvey, Westphalia. 873–85, with later additions *(page 186)*

_____

_____

_____

_____

_____

_____

_____

_____

_____

_____

_____

9-7. *Saint Matthew,* from the *Gospel Book of Charlemagne.* c. 800–10. *(page 188)*

_____

_____

_____

_____

_____

_____

_____

_____

_____

_____

_____

_____

9-8. *Saint Mark,* from the *Gospel Book of Archbishop Ebbo of Reims.* 816–35. *(page 188)*

_____

_____

_____

_____

_____

_____

_____

_____

_____

_____

9-9. Front cover of binding, *Lindau Gospels.* c. 870. *(page 189)*

_____

_____

_____

_____

_____

_____

_____

_____

_____

_____

_____

9-10. *Gero Crucifix.* c. 975–1000. *(page 191)*

_____

_____

_____

_____

_____

_____

_____

_____

_____

_____

_____

9-11. Interior Hildesheim Cathedral (Abbey Church of St. Michael). 1001–33. View toward the apse, after restoration of 1950–60 *(page 192)*

_____

_____

_____

_____

_____

_____

_____

_____

_____

_____

_____

9-12. Reconstructed plan, Hildesheim Cathedral
(page 193)

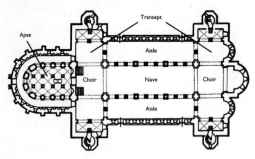

9-13. *Adam and Eve Reproached by the Lord,*
from the Doors of Bishop Bernward,
Hildesheim Cathedral. 1015. *(page 194)*

9-14. *Christ Washing the Feet of Peter,* from
the *Gospel Book of Otto III.* c. 1000. *(page 195)*

Chapter 10
Romanesque Art

10-1. Plan of St-Sernin, Toulouse *(page 199)*

_____

_____

_____

_____

_____

_____

_____

_____

_____

_____

_____

10-2. St-Sernin. c. 1070–1120 *(page 199)*

_____

_____

_____

_____

_____

_____

_____

_____

_____

_____

_____

_____

_____

_____

_____

10-3. Nave and choir, St-Sernin *(page 199)*

_____

_____

_____

_____

_____

_____

_____

_____

_____

_____

10-4. Nave wall, Autun Cathedral. c. 1120–32 *(page 202)*

_____

_____

_____

_____

_____

_____

_____

_____

_____

_____

10-5. West facade, St-Étienne, Caen. Begun 1068 *(page 203)*

_____

_____

_____

_____

_____

_____

_____

_____

_____

_____

10-6. Nave (looking east), Durham Cathedral.
1093–1130 *(page 203)*

10-7. Rib vaults (after Acland) *(page 204)*

10-8. Pisa Baptistery, Cathedral, and Campanile
(view from the west). 1053–1272 *(page 205)*

10-9. Baptistery of S. Giovanni, Florence. c. 1060–1150 *(page 205)*

10-10. *Apostle.* c. 1090. *(page 206)*

10-11. Portion of south portal, St-Pierre, Moissac. Early 12th century *(page 207)*

10-12. Romanesque portal ensembles
(page 207)

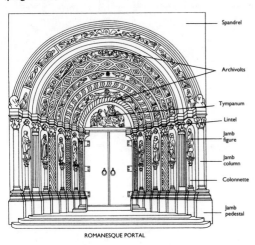

Spandrel

Archivolts

Tympanum

Lintel

Jamb
figure

Jamb
column

Colonnette

Jamb
pedestal

ROMANESQUE PORTAL

10-13. Gislebertus. *Last Judgment,* west tympanum,
Autun Cathedral. c. 1130–35 *(page 208)*

10-14. Renier of Huy. Baptismal font. 1107–18.
(page 209)

10-15. Benedetto Antelami. *King David.* c. 1180–90. *(page 210)*

10-16. *St. John the Evangelist,* from the *Gospel Book of Abbot Wedricus.* c. 1147. *(page 211)*

10-17. *The Battle of Hastings.* Detail of the *Bayeux Tapestry.* c. 1073–83. *(page 213)*

10-18. *The Building of the Tower of Babel*. Detail of painting on the nave vault, St-Savin-sur-Gartempe, France. Early 12th century *(page 213)*

_____

_____

_____

_____

_____

_____

_____

_____

_____

_____

_____

10-19. Nicholas of Verdun. *The Crossing of the Red Sea,* from the *Klosterneuburg Altarpiece*. 1181. *(page 214)*

_____

_____

_____

_____

_____

_____

_____

_____

_____

_____

_____

_____

_____

Chapter 11
Gothic Art

Notes

11-1. Ambulatory, Abbey Church of St-Denis,
Paris. 1140–44 *(page 217)*

_____
_____
_____
_____
_____
_____
_____
_____
_____
_____
_____

11-2. Plan of Notre-Dame, Paris. 1163–c. 1250
(page 220)

_____
_____
_____
_____
_____
_____
_____
_____
_____
_____

11-3. Nave and choir, Notre-Dame, Paris
(page 220)

_____

_____

_____

_____

_____

_____

_____

_____

_____

_____

_____

_____

11-4. Notre-Dame, Paris (view from the
southeast) *(page 220)*

_____

_____

_____

_____

_____

_____

_____

_____

_____

_____

_____

_____

_____

_____

11-5. Axonometric projection of a High Gothic
cathedral (after Acland) *(page 221)*

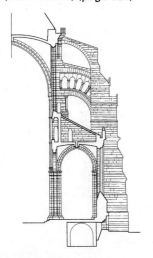

_____

_____

_____

_____

_____

_____

_____

_____

_____

_____

_____

11-6. West facade, Notre-Dame, Paris
(page 221)

11-7. Nave and choir, Chartres Cathedral.
1145–1220 *(page 222)*

11-8. Triforium wall of the nave, Chartres
Cathedral. *(page 223)*

11-9. West facade, Reims Cathedral. c. 1225–99
(page 224)

_____

_____

_____

_____

_____

_____

_____

_____

_____

_____

_____

11-10. West facade, Salisbury Cathedral.
1220–70 *(page 226)*

_____

_____

_____

_____

_____

_____

_____

_____

_____

_____

11-11. Choir, Gloucester Cathedral. 1332–57
(page 226)

_____

_____

_____

_____

_____

_____

_____

_____

_____

11-12. Choir, Heiligenkreuz, Schwäbish-Gmünd, Germany. After 1351 *(page 227)*

11-13. Nave and choir, Abbey Church of Fossanova, Italy. Consecrated 1208 *(page 228)*

11-14. Nave and choir, Sta. Croce, Florence. Begun c. 1295 *(page 229)*

11-15. Florence Cathedral (Sta. Maria del Fiore).
Begun by Arnolfo di Cambio, 1296; dome by
Filippo Brunelleschi, 1420–36 *(page 230)*

11-16. West portal, Chartres Cathedral. c. 1145–70
(page 231)

11-17. Jamb statues, west portal, Chartres
Cathedral *(page 232)*

11-18. *Coronation of the Virgin* (tympanum)
Dormition and Assumption of the Virgin (lintel),
north portal, Chartres Cathedral, c. 1230 *(page 233)*

_____

_____

_____

_____

_____

_____

_____

_____

_____

_____

_____

11-19. Jamb statues, south transept portal,
Chartres Cathedral. c. 1215–20 *(page 234)*

_____

_____

_____

_____

_____

_____

_____

_____

_____

_____

_____

11-20. *Death of the Virgin*, tympanum of
south transept portal, Strasbourg Cathedral.
c. 1220 *(page 235)*

_____

_____

_____

_____

_____

_____

_____

_____

_____

_____

11-21. *Annunciation* and *Visitation*, west
portal, Reims Cathedral. c. 1225–45 *(page 236)*

_____

_____

_____

_____

_____

_____

_____

_____

_____

_____

_____

_____

11-22. *The Virgin of Paris.* Early 14th century.
(page 237)

_____

_____

_____

_____

_____

_____

_____

_____

_____

_____

_____

_____

_____

11-23. *Crucifixion,* on the choir screen,
Naumburg Cathedral. c. 1240–50. *(page 238)*

_____

_____

_____

_____

_____

_____

_____

_____

_____

_____

_____

_____

_____

11-24. *Roettgen Pietà*. Early 14th century. *(page 239)*

11-25. Claus Sluter. *The Moses Well*. 1395–1406. *(page 240)*

11-26. Nicola Pisano. *The Nativity*. Detail of pulpit, Baptistery, Pisa. 1259–60. *(page 241)*

11-27. Giovanni Pisano. *The Nativity*. Detail of
pulpit, Pisa Cathedral. 1302–10. *(page 241)*

11-28. Lorenzo Ghiberti. *The Sacrifice of Isaac.*
1401–2. *(page 242)*

11-29. *Notre Dame de la Belle Verrière,*
Chartres Cathedral. c. 1170. *(page 243)*

11-30. *Nahash the Ammonite Threatening the Jews at Jabesh,* from the *Psalter of Saint Louis.* c. 1260. *(page 244)*

11-31. Duccio. *Christ Entering Jerusalem,* from the back of the *Maestà Altar.* 1308–11. *(page 246)*

11-32. Giotto. Christ Entering Jerusalem. 1305–6. *(page 249)*

11-33. Giotto. *The Lamentation*. Fresco. 1305–6. *(page 250)*

11-34. Simone Martini. *The Road to Calvary.* c. 1340. *(page 252)*

11-35. Pietro Lorenzetti. *Birth of the Virgin.* 1342. *(page 253)*

11-36. Ambrogio Lorenzetti. *The Commune of Siena* (left), *Good Government in the City,* and portion of *Good Government in the Country* (right). 1338–40. *(page 254)*

11-37. Maso Di Banco (att.) (left) and Taddeo Gaddi (right). Tombs of members of the Bardi family. c. 1335–45 and c. 1335–41. *(page 255)*

11-38. Bohemian Master. *Death of the Virgin.* 1350–60. *(page 256)*

11-39. Melchior Broederlam. *Annunciation and Visitation; Presentation in the Temple* and *Flight into Egypt.* 1394–99. *(page 258)*

11-40. The Limbourg Brothers. *October,* from *Les Très Riches Heures du Duc de Berry.* 1413–16. *(page 259)*

11-41. Gentile da Fabriano. *The Adoration of the Magi.* 1423. *(page 261)*

Chapter 12
The Early Renaissance in Italy

Notes

12-1. Nanni di Banco. *Four Saints (Quattro Coronati).* c. 1410–14. *(page 272)*

_____

_____

_____

_____

_____

_____

_____

_____

_____

_____

_____

12-2. Donatello. *St. George* Tabernacle, from Or San Michele, Florence. c. 1415–17. *(page 273)*

_____

_____

_____

_____

_____

_____

_____

_____

_____

_____

12-3. Donatello. *David.* c. 1425–30. *(page 274)*

12-4. Donatello. *Equestrian Monument of Gattamelata.* 1445–50. *(page 275)*

12-5. Lorenzo Ghiberti. *The Story of Jacob and Esau,* panel of the *"Gates of Paradise."* c. 1435. *(page 275)*

12-6. Bernardo Rossellino. Tomb of Leonardo
Bruni. c. 1445–50. *(page 277)*

12-7. Antonio del Pollaiuolo. *Hercules and
Antaeus.* c. 1475. *(page 278)*

12-8. Andrea del Verrocchio. *The Doubting of
Thomas.* 1465–83. *(page 279)*

12-9. Filippo Brunelleschi. S. Lorenzo, Florence. 1421–69 *(page 280)*

12-10. Plan of S. Lorenzo *(page 280)*

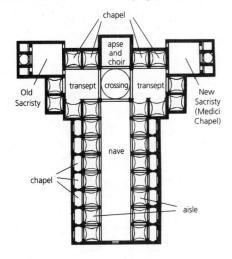

12-11. Leone Battista Alberti. S. Andrea, Mantua. Designed 1470 *(page 283)*

12-12. Giuliano da Sangallo. Sta. Maria delle
Carceri, Prato. Begun 1485 *(page 284)*

12-13. Masaccio. *The Holy Trinity with the
Virgin, St. John, and Two Donors.* Fresco in
Sta. Maria Novella, Florence. 1425 *(page 285)*

12-14. Masaccio. Frescoes on left wall of
Brancacci Chapel, Sta. Maria del Carmine,
Florence. c. 1427 *(page 286)*

12-15. Fra Angelico. *The Deposition.* Probably early 1440s. *(page 288)*

12-16. Domenico Veneziano. *Madonna and Child with Saints.* c. 1455. *(page 289)*

12-17. Piero della Francesca. *The Discovery and Proving of the True Cross.* Fresco in S. Francesco, Arezzo. c. 1452–58 *(page 291)*

12-18. Andrea del Castagno. *David.* c. 1455–57. *(page 292)*

_____

_____

_____

_____

_____

_____

_____

_____

_____

_____

_____

12-19. Sandro Botticelli. *The Birth of Venus.* c. 1480. *(page 293)*

_____

_____

_____

_____

_____

_____

_____

_____

_____

_____

_____

12-20. Domenico Ghirlandaio. *An Old Man and His Grandson.* c. 1480. *(page 294)*

_____

_____

_____

_____

_____

_____

_____

_____

_____

_____

12-21. Pietro Perugino. *The Delivery of the Keys.* Fresco in the Sistine Chapel, the Vatican, Rome. 1482 *(page 295)*

12-22. Andrea Mantegna. *St. Sebastian.* c. 1455–60. *(page 296)*

12-23. Giovanni Bellini. *St. Francis in Ecstasy.* c. 1485. *(page 297)*

Chapter 13
The High Renaissance in Italy

Notes

13-1. Leonardo da Vinci. *The Virgin of the Rocks.* c. 1485. *(page 301)*

13-2. Leonardo da Vinci. *The Last Supper.* Mural in Sta. Maria delle Grazie, Milan. c. 1495–98. *(page 302)*

13-3. Leonardo da Vinci. *Mona Lisa.* c. 1503–5. *(page 303)*

13-4. Leonardo da Vinci. *Project for a Church* (Ms. B). c 1490. *(page 304)*

13-5. Donato Bramante. Original plan for St. Peter's, Rome. 1506 (after Geymuller) *(page 305)*

13-6. Christofor Foppa Caradosso. Bronze medal show-
ing Bramante's design for St. Peter's. 1506. *(page 305)*

_____

_____

_____

_____

_____

_____

_____

_____

_____

_____

_____

_____

13-7. Michelangelo. *David.* 1501–4. *(page 307)*

_____

_____

_____

_____

_____

_____

_____

_____

_____

_____

_____

_____

13-8. Interior of the Sistine Chapel, the Vatican, Rome.
Ceiling frescoes by Michelangelo, 1508–12; *Last
Judgment* on the end wall by Michelangelo, 1534–41;
scenes on the side walls by Perugino, Ghirlandaio,
Botticelli, and others, 1481–82 *(page 308)*

_____

_____

_____

_____

_____

_____

_____

_____

_____

13-9. Michelangelo. *The Creation of Adam,.* detail of fresco on the ceiling of the Sistine Chapel. 1508–12 *(page 309)*

13-10. Michelangelo. *The Last Judgment,* detail of fresco, in the Sistine Chapel. 1534–41 *(page 310)*

13-11. Michelangelo. Tomb of Giuliano de' Medici. 1524–34. *(page 311)*

13-12. Michelangelo. St. Peter's (view from the west), Rome. 1546–64. Dome completed by Giacomo della Porta, 1590 *(page 313)*

13-13. Stanza della Segnatura, with frescoes by Raphael. Vatican Palace, Rome *(page 315)*

13-14. Raphael. *The School of Athens.* Fresco in Stanza della Segnatura, Vatican Palace, Rome. 1510–11 *(page 316)*

Notes

13-15. Raphael. *Galatea.* Fresco in Villa Farnesina, Rome. 1513 *(page 317)*

13-16. Giorgione. *The Tempest.* c. 1505. *(page 318)*

13-17. Titian. *Bacchanal.* c. 1518. *(page 320)*

13-18. Titian. *Danaë.* c. 1544–46. *(page 321)*

_____

_____

_____

_____

_____

_____

_____

_____

_____

_____

_____

13-19. Titian. *Christ Crowned with Thorns.*
c. 1570. *(page 322)*

_____

_____

_____

_____

_____

_____

_____

_____

_____

_____

_____

_____

Chapter 14
The Late Renaissance in Italy

Notes

14-1. Rosso Fiorentino. *The Descent from the Cross.* 1521. *(page 328)*

_____
_____
_____
_____
_____
_____
_____
_____
_____
_____
_____

14-2. Jacopo da Pontormo. *The Deposition.* c. 1526–28. *(page 329)*

_____
_____
_____
_____
_____
_____
_____
_____
_____
_____
_____

14-3. Parmigianino. *The Madonna with the Long Neck.* c. 1535. *(page 330)*

_____

_____

_____

_____

_____

_____

_____

_____

_____

_____

_____

14-4. Agnolo Bronzino. *Allegory of Venus.* c. 1546. *(page 331)*

_____

_____

_____

_____

_____

_____

_____

_____

_____

_____

_____

14-5. Giorgio Vasari. *Perseus and Andromeda.* 1570–72. *(page 332)*

_____

_____

_____

_____

_____

_____

_____

_____

_____

_____

_____

14-6. Girolamo Savoldo. *Saint Matthew and the Angel.* c. 1535. *(page 333)*

_____

_____

_____

_____

_____

_____

_____

_____

_____

_____

_____

14-7. Correggio. *The Assumption of the Virgin.* Portion of fresco in the dome of Parma Cathedral. c. 1525 *(page 334)*

_____

_____

_____

_____

_____

_____

_____

_____

_____

_____

_____

14-8. Correggio. *Jupiter and Io.* c. 1532. *(page 335)*

_____

_____

_____

_____

_____

_____

_____

_____

_____

_____

_____

_____

14-9. Paolo Veronese. *Christ in the House of Levi.* 1573. *(page 336)*

14-10. Jacopo Tintoretto. *The Last Supper.* 1592–94. *(page 337)*

14-11. El Greco. *The Burial of Count Orgaz.* 1586. *(page 338)*

14-12. Chapel with *The Burial of Count Orgaz.*
Sto. Tomé, Toledo, Spain *(page 339)*

_____

_____

_____

_____

_____

_____

_____

_____

_____

_____

_____

14-13. Benvenuto Cellini. *Saltcellar of Francis I.*
c. 1543. *(page 340)*

_____

_____

_____

_____

_____

_____

_____

_____

_____

_____

_____

_____

_____

14-14. Francesco Primaticcio. *Stucco Figures.*
c. 1541–45. *(page 341)*

_____

_____

_____

_____

_____

_____

_____

_____

_____

_____

_____

14-15. Giovanni Bologna. *The Abduction of the Sabine Woman.* Completed 1583. *(page 342)*

14-16. Giulio Romano. Courtyard, Palazzo del Te, Mantua. 1527–34 *(page 343)*

14-17. Andrea Palladio. Villa Rotonda, Vicenza. c. 1567–70 *(page 344)*

14-18. Giacomo della Porta. Facade of Il Gesù,
Rome. c. 1575–84 *(page 345)*

_____

_____

_____

_____

_____

_____

_____

_____

_____

_____

Chapter 15
"Late Gothic" Painting, Sculpture, and Graphic Arts

Notes

15-1. Robert Campin (Master of Flémalle).
Mérode Altarpiece. c. 1425–30. *(page 348)*

_____

_____

_____

_____

_____

_____

_____

_____

_____

_____

_____

15-2. Hubert and/or Jan van Eyck. *The
Crucifixion* and *The Last Judgment.* c. 1420–25.
(page 351)

_____

_____

_____

_____

_____

_____

_____

_____

_____

_____

_____

15-3. Jan van Eyck. *The Arnolfini Betrothal.*
1434. *(page 352)*

15-4. Jan van Eyck. Detail of *The Arnolfini Betrothal (page 353)*

15-5. Rogier van der Weyden. *Descent from the Cross.* c. 1435. *(page 354)*

15-6. Hugo van der Goes. *Portinari Altarpiece*
(open). c. 1476. *(page 355)*

_____

_____

_____

_____

_____

_____

_____

_____

_____

_____

_____

15-7. Hieronymus Bosch. *The Garden of
Delights.* c. 1510–15. *(page 356)*

_____

_____

_____

_____

_____

_____

_____

_____

_____

_____

15-8. Conrad Witz. *The Miraculous Draught of
Fishes.* 1444. *(page 358)*

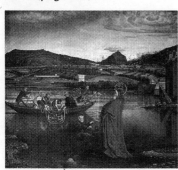

_____

_____

_____

_____

_____

_____

_____

_____

_____

_____

15-9. Jean Fouquet. *Étienne Chevalier and St. Stephen,* left wing of the *Melun Diptych.* c. 1450. *(page 359)*

_____

_____

_____

_____

_____

_____

_____

_____

_____

_____

_____

15-10. Jean Fouquet. *Madonna and Child,* right wing of the *Melun Diptych.* c. 1450. *(page 359)*

_____

_____

_____

_____

_____

_____

_____

_____

_____

_____

_____

15-11. Michael Pacher. *St. Wolfgang Altarpiece.* 1471–81. *(page 360)*

_____

_____

_____

_____

_____

_____

_____

_____

_____

_____

_____

15-12. *Saint Dorothy.* c. 1420. *(page 362)*

_____
_____
_____
_____
_____
_____
_____
_____
_____
_____
_____

15-13. Martin Schongauer. *Temptation of Saint Anthony.* c. 1480–90. *(page 363)*

_____
_____
_____
_____
_____
_____
_____
_____
_____
_____
_____

Chapter 16
The Renaissance in the North

Notes

16-1. Matthias Grünewald. *The Crucifixion,* from the *Isenheim Altarpiece* (fully closed, central section). c. 1509/10–15. *(page 367)*

16-2. Matthias Grünewald. *The Annunciation; The Madonna and Child with Angels,* and *The Resurrection,* from the *Isenheim Altarpiece* (half closed). c. 1510–15. *(page 367)*

16-3. Albrecht Dürer. *Self-Portrait.* 1500.
(page 368)

_____

_____

_____

_____

_____

_____

_____

_____

_____

_____

_____

16-4. Albrecht Dürer. *Adam and Eve.* 1504.
(page 369)

_____

_____

_____

_____

_____

_____

_____

_____

_____

_____

_____

_____

16-5. Albrecht Dürer. *Knight, Death, and Devil.*
1513. *(page 369)*

_____

_____

_____

_____

_____

_____

_____

_____

_____

_____

_____

16-6. Lucas Cranach the Elder. *The Judgment of Paris.* 1530. *(page 371)*

_____

_____

_____

_____

_____

_____

_____

_____

_____

_____

16-7. Albrecht Altdorfer. *The Battle of Issus.* 1529. *(page 372)*

_____

_____

_____

_____

_____

_____

_____

_____

_____

_____

_____

16-8. Hans Holbein the Younger. *Erasmus of Rotterdam.* c. 1523. *(page 373)*

_____

_____

_____

_____

_____

_____

_____

_____

_____

_____

16-9. Hans Holbein the Younger. *Henry VIII.*
1540. *(page 374)*

_____

_____

_____

_____

_____

_____

_____

_____

_____

_____

16-10. Jan Gossaert. *Danaë,* 1527. *(page 376)*

_____

_____

_____

_____

_____

_____

_____

_____

_____

_____

_____

_____

16-11. Joachim Patinir. *Landscape with St.
Jerome Removing the Thorn from the Lion's
Paw.* c. 1520. *(page 377)*

_____

_____

_____

_____

_____

_____

_____

_____

_____

16-12. Pieter Aertsen. *The Meat Stall.* 1551.
(page 377)

_____

_____

_____

_____

_____

_____

_____

_____

_____

_____

16-13. Pieter Bruegel the Elder. *The Return of the Hunters.* 1565. *(page 379)*

_____

_____

_____

_____

_____

_____

_____

_____

16-14. Pieter Bruegel the Elder. *Peasant Wedding.* c. 1565. *(page 379)*

_____

_____

_____

_____

_____

_____

_____

_____

_____

16-15. Pierre Lescot. Square Court of the
Louvre, Paris. Begun 1546 *(page 380)*

_____

_____

_____

_____

_____

_____

_____

_____

_____

_____

16-16. Jean Goujon. Reliefs from the Fontaine
des Innocents, Paris. 1548–49 *(page 381)*

_____

_____

_____

_____

_____

_____

_____

_____

_____

Chapter 17
The Baroque in Italy and Spain

Notes

17-1. Caravaggio. *The Calling of Saint Matthew.* c. 1599–1602. *(page 385)*

17-2. Jusepe Ribera. *St. Jerome and the Angel of Judgment.* 1626. *(page 386)*

17-3. Artemisia Gentileschi. *Judith and Her Maidservant with the Head of Holofernes.* c. 1625. *(page 387)*

_____

_____

_____

_____

_____

_____

_____

_____

_____

_____

_____

17-4. Annibale Carracci. Ceiling fresco in the Gallery, Palazzo Farnese, Rome. 1597–1604 *(page 388)*

_____

_____

_____

_____

_____

_____

_____

_____

_____

_____

_____

_____

17-5. Guido Reni. *Aurora.* Ceiling fresco in the Casino Rospigliosi, Rome. 1613 *(page 390)*

_____

_____

_____

_____

_____

_____

_____

_____

_____

_____

17-6. Guercino. *Aurora.* Ceiling fresco in the
Villa Rudovisi, Rome. 1613 *(page 390)*

17-7. Pietro da Cortona. *The Glorification of
the Reign of Urban VIII.* 1633–39. *(page 391)*

17-8. St. Peter's, Rome. Nave and facade by
Carlo Maderno, 1607–15; colonnade by
Gianlorenzo Bernini, designed 1657 *(page 392)*

17-9. Francesco Borromini. Facade, S. Carlo alle
Quattro Fontane, Rome. 1665–67 *(page 394)*

17-10. Dome, S. Carlo alle Quattro Fontane
(page 395)

17-11. Francesco Borromini. Sta. Agnese in
Piazza Navona, Rome. 1653–63 *(page 395)*

17-12. Guarino Guarini. Dome of Chapel of the Holy
Shroud, Turin Cathedral. 1668–94 *(page 396)*

17-13. Gianlorenzo Bernini. *David.* 1623.
(page 397)

17-14. Gianlorenzo Bernini. *The Ecstasy of
Saint Theresa.* 1645–52. *(page 398)*

17-15. Anonymous. *The Cornaro Chapel.* 18th
century. *(page 398)*

17-16. Alessandro Algardi. *The Meeting of
Pope Leo I and Attila.* 1646. *(page 399)*

17-17. Francisco de Zurbarán. *Saint Serapion.*
1628. *(page 400)*

17-18. Diego Velázquez. *The Maids of Honor.*
1656. *(page 401)*

_____

_____

_____

_____

_____

_____

_____

_____

_____

_____

_____

17-19. Bartolomé Esteban Murillo. *Virgin and
Child.* c. 1675–80. *(page 402)*

_____

_____

_____

_____

_____

_____

_____

_____

_____

_____

_____

_____

Chapter 18
The Baroque in Flanders and Holland

Notes

18-1. Peter Paul Rubens. *The Raising of the Cross.* 1609–10. *(page 405)*

_____

_____

_____

_____

_____

_____

_____

_____

_____

_____

18-2. Peter Paul Rubens. *Marie de' Medici, Queen of France, Landing in Marseilles.* 1622–23. *(page 405)*

_____

_____

_____

_____

_____

_____

_____

_____

_____

_____

_____

_____

18-3. Peter Paul Rubens. *The Garden of Love.*
c. 1638. *(page 406)*

18-4. Anthony van Dyck. *Rinaldo and Armida.*
1629. *(page 407)*

18-5. Anthony van Dyck. *Portrait of Charles I
Hunting.* c. 1635. *(page 408)*

18-6. Jacob Jordaens. *Homage to Pomona*
(Allegory of Fruitfulness). c. 1623. *(page 409)*

_____

_____

_____

_____

_____

_____

_____

_____

_____

_____

_____

18-7. Frans Hals. *The Jolly Toper.* c. 1628–30.
(page 410)

_____

_____

_____

_____

_____

_____

_____

_____

_____

_____

_____

18-8. Judith Leyster. *Boy Playing a Flute.*
1630–35. *(page 410)*

_____

_____

_____

_____

_____

_____

_____

_____

_____

_____

_____

18-9. Rembrandt van Rijn. *The Blinding of Samson.* 1636. *(page 411)*

18-10. Rembrandt van Rijn. *The Night Watch (The Company of Captain Frans Banning Cocq).* 1642. *(page 412)*

18-11. Rembrandt van Rijn. *Self-Portrait.* 1658. *(page 413)*

18-12. Rembrandt van Rijn. *Christ Preaching.* c. 1652. *(page 414)*

18-13. Jacob van Ruisdael. *The Jewish Cemetery.* 1655–60. *(page 415)*

18-14. Willem Claesz Heda. *Still Life.* 1634. *(page 416)*

18-15. Jan Steen. *The Feast of Saint Nicholas.*
c. 1660–65. *(page 417)*

_____

_____

_____

_____

_____

_____

_____

_____

_____

_____

18-16. Jan Vermeer. *The Letter.* 1666. *(page 419)*

_____

_____

_____

_____

_____

_____

_____

_____

_____

_____

Chapter 19
The Baroque in France and England

Notes

19-1. Georges de La Tour. *Joseph the Carpenter.* c. 1645. *(page 421)*

_____

_____

_____

_____

_____

_____

_____

_____

_____

_____

19-2. Nicolas Poussin. *The Abduction of the Sabine Women.* c. 1633–34. *(page 422)*

_____

_____

_____

_____

_____

_____

_____

_____

_____

_____

_____

19-3. Claude Lorraine. *A Pastoral Landscape.*
c. 1650. *(page 423)*

_____

_____

_____

_____

_____

_____

_____

_____

_____

_____

19-4. Simon Vouet. *The Toilet of Venus.* c. 1640.
(page 424)

_____

_____

_____

_____

_____

_____

_____

_____

_____

_____

_____

19-5. Claude Perrault. East front of the Louvre,
Paris. 1667–70 *(page 426)*

_____

_____

_____

_____

_____

_____

_____

_____

_____

_____

19-6. Louis Le Vau and Jules Hardouin-Mansart. Garden front of the center block of the Palace of Versailles. 1669–85 *(page 427)*

19-7. Jules Hardouin-Mansart, Charles Lebrun, and Antoine Coysevox. Salon de la Guerre, Palace of Versailles. Begun 1678 *(page 428)*

19-8. Charles Rivière. *Perspective View of the Château and Gardens of Versailles.* Lithograph after an 1860 photograph *(page 429)*

19-9. Jules Hardouin-Mansart. Church of the
Invalides, Paris. 1680–91 *(page 430)*

_____

_____

_____

_____

_____

_____

_____

_____

_____

_____

19-10. Plan of the Church of the Invalides
(page 430)

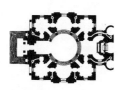

_____

_____

_____

_____

_____

_____

_____

_____

_____

_____

19-11. Antoine Coysevox. *Charles Lebrun.*
1676. *(page 431)*

_____

_____

_____

_____

_____

_____

_____

_____

_____

_____

19-12. Pierre-Paul Puget. *Milo of Crotona.* 1671–83. *(page 431)*

19-13. Inigo Jones. West front of the Banqueting House, Whitehall Palace, London. 1619–22 *(page 432)*

19-14. Sir Christopher Wren. Facade of St. Paul's Cathedral, London. 1675–1710 *(page 433)*

Chapter 20
The Rococo

Notes

20-1. The Varengeville Room. From the Hôtel de Varengeville, 217, boulevard St-Germain, Paris. c. 1740. *(page 436)*

_____

_____

_____

_____

_____

_____

_____

_____

_____

_____

_____

20-2. Jean-Baptiste Pigalle. Tomb of the Maréchal de Saxe. 1753–76. *(page 437)*

_____

_____

_____

_____

_____

_____

_____

_____

_____

_____

20-3. Jean-Antoine Watteau. *A Pilgrimage to Cythera.* 1717. *(page 438)*

20-4. Jean-Antoine Watteau. *Gilles and Four Other Characters from the Commedia dell'Arte (Pierrot).* c. 1719. *(page 438)*

20-5. François Boucher. *The Toilet of Venus.* 1751. *(page 439)*

20-6. Jean-Baptiste-Siméon Chardin. *Back from the Market.* 1739. *(page 440)*

_____

_____

_____

_____

_____

_____

_____

_____

_____

_____

_____

20-7. Marie-Louise-Élisabeth Vigée-Lebrun. *The Duchesse de Polignac.* 1783. *(page 441)*

_____

_____

_____

_____

_____

_____

_____

_____

_____

_____

_____

_____

_____

20-8. William Hogarth. *The Orgy,* Scene III of *The Rake's Progress.* c. 1734. *(page 442)*

_____

_____

_____

_____

_____

_____

_____

_____

_____

_____

_____

_____

_____

20-9. Thomas Gainsborough. *Mrs. Siddons.*
1785. *(page 443)*

20-10. Sir Joshua Reynolds. *Mrs. Siddons as
the Tragic Muse.* 1784. *(page 443)*

20-11. Johann Fischer von Erlach. Facade of
St. Charles Borromaeus (Karlskirche), Vienna.
1716–37 *(page 445)*

20-12. Balthasar Neumann. The Kaisersaal,
Residenz, Würzburg, Germany. 1719–44. Frescoes
by Giovanni Battista Tiepolo, 1751 *(page 446)*

20-13. Canaletto. *The Bucintoro at the Molo.*
c. 1732. *(page 448)*

20-14. Giovanni Battista Piranesi. *Tower with
Bridges,* from *Prison Caprices.* 1760–61. *(page 449)*

Chapter 21
Neoclassicism

Notes

21-1. Jean-Baptiste Greuze. *The Village Bride.*
1761. *(page 460)*

_____

_____

_____

_____

_____

_____

_____

_____

_____

_____

_____

21-2. Jacques-Louis David. *The Death of
Socrates.* 1787. *(page 461)*

_____

_____

_____

_____

_____

_____

_____

_____

_____

_____

_____

21-3. Jacques-Louis David. *The Death of Marat.*
1793. *(page 461)*

_____

_____

_____

_____

_____

_____

_____

_____

_____

_____

_____

21-4. Benjamin West. *The Death of General
Wolfe.* 1770. *(page 462)*

_____

_____

_____

_____

_____

_____

_____

_____

_____

_____

_____

_____

_____

21-5. John Singleton Copley. *Paul Revere.*
c. 1768–70. *(page 463)*

_____

_____

_____

_____

_____

_____

_____

_____

_____

_____

_____

_____

21-6. Francis-Xavier Vispré (attr.). *Portrait of Louis-François Roubiliac.* c. 1750. *(page 464)*

_____

_____

_____

_____

_____

_____

_____

_____

_____

_____

_____

21-7. John Singleton Copley. *Watson and the Shark.* 1778. *(page 465)*

_____

_____

_____

_____

_____

_____

_____

_____

_____

_____

_____

21-8. Angelica Kauffmann. *The Artist in the Character of Design Listening to the Inspiration of Poetry.* 1782. *(page 466)*

_____

_____

_____

_____

_____

_____

_____

_____

_____

_____

_____

21-9. Jean-Antoine Houdon. *Voltaire Seated.*
1781. *(page 467)*

21-10. Lord Burlington and William Kent. Chiswick
House, near London. Begun 1725 *(page 469)*

21-11. Jacques-Germain Soufflot. The Panthéon
(Ste-Geneviève), Paris. 1755–92 *(page 471)*

21-12. Robert Adam. The Library, Kenwood, London. 1767–69 *(page 473)*

21-13. Thomas Jefferson. Monticello, Charlottesville, Virginia. 1770–84; 1796–1806 *(page 474)*

Chapter 22
Romanticism

22-1. Francisco Goya. *The Family of Charles IV.* 1800. *(page 477)*

22-2. Francisco Goya. *The Third of May, 1808.* 1814. *(page 478)*

22-3. Antoine-Jean Gros. *Napoleon in the Pesthouse at Jaffa, 11 March 1799.* 1804. *(page 480)*

22-4. Théodore Géricault. *The Raft of the "Medusa."* 1818–19. *(page 481)*

22-5. Jean-Auguste-Dominique Ingres. *Odalisque with a Slave.* 1839–40. *(page 482)*

22-6. Jean-Auguste-Dominique Ingres. *Louis Bertin.* 1832. *(page 483)*

22-7. Eugène Delacroix. *The Death of Sardanapalus.* 1827. *(page 484)*

22-8. Eugène Delacroix. *Women of Algiers.* 1834. *(page 485)*

22-9. Eugène Delacroix. *The Abduction of Rebecca.* 1846. *(page 486)*

_____
_____
_____
_____
_____
_____
_____
_____
_____
_____
_____

22-10. Honoré Daumier. *The Third-Class Carriage.* c. 1862. *(page 488)*

_____
_____
_____
_____
_____
_____
_____
_____
_____

22-11. Camille Corot. *View of Rome: The Bridge and Castel Sant'Angelo with the Cupola of St. Peter's.* 1826–27. *(page 489)*

_____
_____
_____
_____
_____
_____
_____
_____
_____
_____

22-12. François Millet. *The Sower.* c. 1850.
(page 490)

22-13. Rosa Bonheur. *Plowing in the Nivernais.*
1849. *(page 491)*

22-14. John Henry Fuseli. *The Nightmare.* c. 1790.
(page 491)

22-15. William Blake. *The Ancient of Days,* frontispiece to *Europe, A Prophesy.* 1794. *(page 492)*

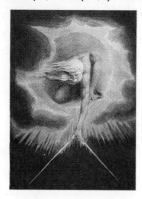

22-16. John Constable. *The Haywain.* 1821. *(page 493)*

22-17. Joseph Mallord William Turner. *The Slave Ship.* 1840. *(page 494)*

22-18. Caspar David Friedrich. *The Polar Sea.*
1824. *(page 495)*

22-19. Thomas Cole. *View of Schroon Mountain,
Essex County, New York, after a Storm.* 1838.
(page 496)

22-20. George Caleb Bingham. *Fur Traders
Descending the Missouri.* c. 1845. *(page 497)*

22-21. Antonio Canova. Tomb of the Archduchess
Maria Christina. 1798–1805. *(page 499)*

22-22. François Rude. *La Marseillaise.* 1833–36.
(page 500)

22-23. Jean-Baptiste Carpeaux. *The Dance.*
1867–69. *(page 501)*

22-24. Auguste Bartholdi. *Liberty Enlightening the World (The Statue of Liberty).* 1875–84. *(page 502)*

22-25. Karl Friedrich Schinkel. Altes Museum, Berlin. 1824–28 *(page 503)*

22-26. Horace Walpole, with William Robinson and others. Strawberry Hill, Twickenham, England. 1749–77 *(page 504)*

22-27. Sir Charles Barry and A. N. Welby
Pugin. The Houses of Parliament, London.
Begun 1836 *(page 505)*

22-28. Charles Garnier. The Opéra, Paris.
1861–74 *(page 505)*

22-29. Joseph-Nicéphore Niépce. *View from
His Window at Le Gras.* 1826. *(page 507)*

22-30. Nadar. *Sarah Bernhardt.* 1859. *(page 508)*

_____

_____

_____

_____

_____

_____

_____

_____

_____

_____

_____

_____

22-31. *Czar Cannon outside the Spassky Gate, Moscow.* (cast 1586; presently inside the Kremlin). Second half of 19th century. *(page 509)*

_____

_____

_____

_____

_____

_____

_____

_____

_____

_____

_____

_____

_____

22-32. Alexander Gardner. *Home of a Rebel Sharpshooter, Gettysburg.* July 1863. *(page 510)*

_____

_____

_____

_____

_____

_____

_____

_____

_____

_____

_____

Chapter 23
Realism and Impressionism

Notes

23-1. Gustave Courbet. *Burial at Ornans.* 1849. *(page 513)*

_____

_____

_____

_____

_____

_____

_____

_____

_____

_____

_____

23-2. Gustave Courbet. *Studio of a Painter: A Real Allegory Summarizing My Seven Years of Life as an Artist.* 1854–55. *(page 513)*

_____

_____

_____

_____

_____

_____

_____

_____

_____

_____

23-3. Édouard Manet. *Luncheon on the Grass
(Le Déjeuner sur l'Herbe).* 1863. *(page 514)*

23-4. Marcantonio Raimondi, after Raphael.
The Judgment of Paris. c. 1520. *(page 515)*

23-5. *River Gods.* Detail of Roman sarcophagus.
3rd century A.D. *(page 515)*

23-6. Édouard Manet. *The Fifer.* 1866. *(page 516)*

23-7. Claude Monet. *On the Bank of the Seine, Bennecourt.* 1868. *(page 517)*

23-8. Claude Monet. *Red Boats, Argenteuil.* 1875. *(page 518)*

Notes

23-9. Auguste Renoir. *Luncheon of the Boating Party, Bourigval.* 1881. *(page 519)*

23-10. Edgar Degas. *The Glass of Absinthe.* 1876. *(page 520)*

23-11. Edgar Degas. *The Tub.* 1886. *(page 520)*

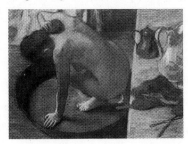

23-12. Berthe Morisot. *The Cradle.* 1872.
(page 521)

23-13. Mary Cassatt. *The Bath.* 1891–92.
(page 522)

23-14. Claude Monet. *Water Lilies.* 1907.
(page 523)

Notes

23-15. Dante Gabriel Rossetti. *Beata Beatrix.* 1872. *(page 524)*

_____

_____

_____

_____

_____

_____

_____

_____

_____

_____

23-16. William Morris (Morris & Co.). Green Dining Room. 1867. *(page 525)*

_____

_____

_____

_____

_____

_____

_____

_____

_____

_____

_____

_____

23-17. James Abbott McNeill Whistler. *Arrangement in Black and Gray: The Artist's Mother.* 1871. *(page 525)*

_____

_____

_____

_____

_____

_____

_____

_____

_____

_____

23-18. James Abbott McNeill Whistler. *Nocturne in Black and Gold: The Falling Rocket.* c. 1874. *(page 526)*

_____

_____

_____

_____

_____

_____

_____

_____

_____

23-19. Winslow Homer. *Snap the Whip.* 1872. *(page 527)*

_____

_____

_____

_____

_____

_____

_____

_____

_____

_____

23-20. Thomas Eakins. *William Rush Carving His Allegorical Figure of the Schuylkill River.* 1877. *(page 528)*

_____

_____

_____

_____

_____

_____

_____

_____

_____

_____

_____

23-21. Henry O. Tanner. *The Banjo Lesson.* c. 1893. *(page 528)*

23-22. Auguste Rodin. *The Thinker.* 1879–89. *(page 529)*

23-23. Auguste Rodin. *Monument to Balzac.* 1897–98. *(page 530)*

23-24. Edgar Degas. *The Little Fourteen-Year-Old Dancer.* 1878–80. *(page 531)*

23-25. Henri Labrouste. Bibliothèque Ste-Geneviève, Paris. 1843–50 *(page 533)*

23-26. Henri Labrouste. Reading Room, Bibliothèque Ste-Geneviève *(page 533)*

23-27. Sir Joseph Paxton. The Crystal Palace,
London. 1851; reerected in Sydenham 1852;
destroyed 1936. *(page 536)*

_____

_____

_____

_____

_____

_____

_____

_____

_____

_____

23-28. Gustave Eiffel. The Eiffel Tower, Paris.
1887–89 *(page 537)*

_____

_____

_____

_____

_____

_____

_____

_____

_____

_____

Chapter 24
Post-Impressionism, Symbolism, and Art Nouveau

Notes

24-1. Paul Cézanne. *Still Life with Apples.*
1879–82. *(page 539)*

_____

_____

_____

_____

_____

_____

_____

_____

_____

_____

_____

24-2. Paul Cézanne. *Mont Ste-Victoire Seen
from Bibémus Quarry.* c. 1897–1900. *(page 540)*

_____

_____

_____

_____

_____

_____

_____

_____

_____

_____

24-3. Georges Seurat. *A Sunday Afternoon on the Island of La Grande Jatte.* 1884–86. *(page 541)*

_____

_____

_____

_____

_____

_____

_____

_____

_____

24-4. Vincent van Gogh. *Wheat Field and Cypress Trees.* 1889. *(page 543)*

_____

_____

_____

_____

_____

_____

_____

_____

_____

_____

_____

24-5. Vincent van Gogh. *Self-Portrait.* 1889. *(page 543)*

_____

_____

_____

_____

_____

_____

_____

_____

_____

_____

_____

24-6. Paul Gauguin. *The Vision after the Sermon (Jacob Wrestling with the Angel).* 1888. *(page 544)*

24-7. Paul Gauguin. *Where Do We Come From? What Are We? Where Are We Going?* 1897. *(page 545)*

24-8. Henri de Toulouse-Lautrec. *At the Moulin Rouge.* 1893–95. *(page 546)*

24-9. Édouard Vuillard. *Interior at l'Étang-la-Ville (The Suitor).* 1893. *(page 547)*

_____

_____

_____

_____

_____

_____

_____

_____

_____

_____

24-10. Gustave Moreau. *The Apparition (Dance of Salomé).* c. 1876. *(page 547)*

_____

_____

_____

_____

_____

_____

_____

_____

_____

_____

24-11. Aubrey Beardsley. *Salome.* 1892. *(page 548)*

_____

_____

_____

_____

_____

_____

_____

_____

_____

_____

_____

24-12. Odilon Redon. *The Eye like a Strange Balloon Mounts toward Infinity,* from the series Edgar A. Poe. 1882. *(page 548)*

_____
_____
_____
_____
_____
_____
_____
_____
_____
_____
_____

24-13. Edvard Munch. *The Scream.* 1893. *(page 549)*

_____
_____
_____
_____
_____
_____
_____
_____
_____
_____

24-14. Pablo Picasso. *The Old Guitarist.* 1903. *(page 550)*

_____
_____
_____
_____
_____
_____
_____
_____
_____
_____

24-15. Henri Rousseau. *The Dream*. 1910.
(page 551)

_____

_____

_____

_____

_____

_____

_____

_____

_____

_____

_____

24-16. Paula Modersohn-Becker. *Self-Portrait*.
1906. *(page 552)*

_____

_____

_____

_____

_____

_____

_____

_____

_____

_____

_____

24-17. Aristide Maillol. *Seated Woman (La
Méditerranée)*. c. 1901. *(page 552)*

_____

_____

_____

_____

_____

_____

_____

_____

_____

_____

_____

24-18. Ernst Barlach. *Man Drawing a Sword.*
1911. *(page 553)*

_____

_____

_____

_____

_____

_____

_____

_____

_____

_____

24-19. Antoní Gaudí. Casa Milá Apartments,
Barcelona. 1905–7 *(page 555)*

_____

_____

_____

_____

_____

_____

_____

_____

_____

_____

24-20. Charles Rennie Mackintosh. North
façade of the Glasgow School of Art, Glasgow,
Scotland. 1896–1910 *(page 555)*

_____

_____

_____

_____

_____

_____

_____

_____

_____

_____

24-21. Henri van de Velde. Theater, Werkbund
Exhibition, Cologne. 1914. Destroyed *(page 555)*

_____

_____

_____

_____

_____

_____

_____

_____

_____

_____

_____

24-22. Louis Sullivan. Wainwright Building, St.
Louis, Missouri. 1890–91. Destroyed *(page 556)*

_____

_____

_____

_____

_____

_____

_____

_____

_____

_____

_____

_____

_____

24-23. Jacob Riis. *Bandits' Roost.* c. 1888.
(page 557)

_____

_____

_____

_____

_____

_____

_____

_____

_____

_____

_____

_____

_____

24-24. Oscar Rejlander. *The Two Paths of Life.* 1857. *(page 558)*

_____

_____

_____

_____

_____

_____

_____

_____

_____

_____

_____

_____

24-25. Julia Margaret Cameron. *Ellen Terry, at the Age of 16.* c. 1863. *(page 558)*

_____

_____

_____

_____

_____

_____

_____

_____

_____

_____

_____

_____

24-26. Gertrude Käsebier. *The Magic Crystal.* c. 1904. *(page 558)*

_____

_____

_____

_____

_____

_____

_____

_____

_____

_____

_____

_____

24-27. Edward Steichen. *Rodin with His
Sculptures "Victor Hugo" and "The Thinker."*
1902. *(page 559)*

_____

_____

_____

_____

_____

_____

_____

_____

_____

_____

24-28. Eadweard Muybridge. *Female Semi-
Nude in Motion,* from *Human and Animal
Locomotion,* vol. 2, pl. 271. 1887. *(page 560)*

_____

_____

_____

_____

_____

_____

_____

_____

_____

_____

Chapter 25
Twentieth-Century Painting

Notes

25-1. Henri Matisse. *The Joy of Life*. 1905–6.
(page 563)

_____
_____
_____
_____
_____
_____
_____
_____
_____
_____
_____

25-2. Henri Matisse. *The Red Studio*. 1911.
(page 564)

_____
_____
_____
_____
_____
_____
_____
_____
_____
_____
_____

25-3. Georges Rouault. *The Old King*. 1916–37. *(page 565)*

25-4. Ernst Ludwig Kirchner. *Self-Portrait with Model*. 1907. *(page 565)*

25-5. Oskar Kokoschka. *The Bride of the Wind*. 1914. *(page 566)*

25-6. Wassily Kandinsky. *Sketch I for "Composition VII."* 1913. *(page 567)*

25-7. Marsden Hartley. *Portrait of a German Officer.* 1914. *(page 568)*

25-8. Pablo Picasso. *Les Demoiselles d'Avignon.* 1907. *(page 570)*

25-9. Pablo Picasso. *Portrait of Ambroise Vollard.* 1910. *(page 571)*

25-10. Georges Braque. *Newspaper, Bottle, Packet of Tobacco (Le Courrier).* 1914. *(page 572)*

25-11. Umberto Boccioni. *Dynamism of a Cyclist.* 1913. *(page 573)*

25-12. Liubov Popova. *The Traveler.* 1915.
(page 574)

25-13. Kazimir Malevich. *Suprematist Composition: White on White.* 1918. *(page 575)*

25-14. Giorgio de Chirico. *Mystery and Melancholy of a Street.* 1914. *(page 575)*

25-15. Marc Chagall. *I and the Village.* 1911.
(page 576)

25-16. Marcel Duchamp. *The Bride.* 1912.
(page 577)

25-17. George Bellows. *Stag at Sharkey's.*
1909. *(page 577)*

25-18. Pablo Picasso. *Three Musicians.*
Summer 1921. *(page 579)*

_____

_____

_____

_____

_____

_____

_____

_____

_____

_____

25-19. Pablo Picasso. *Three Dancers.* 1925.
(page 580)

_____

_____

_____

_____

_____

_____

_____

_____

_____

_____

_____

25-20. Pablo Picasso. *Guernica.* 1937. *(page 580)*

_____

_____

_____

_____

_____

_____

_____

_____

_____

_____

25-21. Henri Matisse. *Decorative Figure against an Ornamental Background.* 1927. *(page 581)*

25-22. Fernand Léger. *The City.* 1919. *(page 582)*

25-23. Charles Demuth. *I Saw the Figure 5 in Gold.* 1928. *(page 582)*

25-24. Piet Mondrian. *Composition with Red, Blue, and Yellow.* 1930. *(page 583)*

_____

_____

_____

_____

_____

_____

_____

_____

_____

_____

25-25. Max Ernst. *1 Copper Plate 1 Zinc Plate 1 Rubber Cloth 2 Calipers 1 Drainpipe Telescope 1 Piping Man.* 1920. *(page 585)*

_____

_____

_____

_____

_____

_____

_____

_____

_____

_____

25-26. Max Ernst. *La Toilette de la Mariée.* 1940. *(page 585)*

_____

_____

_____

_____

_____

_____

_____

_____

_____

_____

25-27. Joan Miró. *Composition.* 1933. *(page 586)*

_____

_____

_____

_____

_____

_____

_____

_____

_____

_____

25-28. Paul Klee. *Twittering Machine.* 1922. *(page 587)*

_____

_____

_____

_____

_____

_____

_____

_____

_____

_____

_____

_____

25-29. Käthe Kollwitz. *Never Again War!* 1924. *(page 588)*

_____

_____

_____

_____

_____

_____

_____

_____

_____

_____

_____

25-30. George Grosz. *Germany, a Winter's Tale*. 1918. *(page 588)*

25-31. Max Beckmann. *Departure*. 1932–33. *(page 589)*

25-32. Georgia O'Keeffe. *Black Iris III*. 1926. *(page 590)*

25-33. Edward Hopper. *Early Sunday Morning.*
1930. *(page 591)*

25-34. Arshile Gorky. *The Liver Is the Cock's
Comb.* 1944. *(page 592)*

25-35. Jackson Pollock. *Autumn Rhythm:
Number 30, 1950.* 1950. *(page 593)*

25-36. Lee Krasner. *Celebration.* 1959–60. *(page 594)*

25-37. Willem de Kooning. *Woman II.* 1952. *(page 594)*

25-38. Jean Dubuffet. *Le Métafisyx,* from the Corps de Dames series. 1950. *(page 595)*

25-39. Francis Bacon. *Head Surrounded by Sides of Beef*. 1954. *(page 596)*

25-40. Mark Rothko. *White and Greens in Blue*. 1957. *(page 597)*

25-41. Ellsworth Kelly. *Red Blue Green*. 1963. *(page 597)*

25-42. Frank Stella. *Empress of India*. 1965.
(page 598)

_____

_____

_____

_____

_____

_____

_____

_____

_____

_____

_____

25-43. Romare Bearden. *The Prevalence of
Ritual: Baptism*. 1964. *(page 599)*

_____

_____

_____

_____

_____

_____

_____

_____

_____

_____

_____

_____

25-44. Richard Anuszkiewicz. *Entrance to
Green*. 1970. *(page 599)*

_____

_____

_____

_____

_____

_____

_____

_____

_____

_____

_____

25-45. Jasper Johns. *Three Flags.* 1958. *(page 601)*

25-46. Roy Lichtenstein. *Drowning Girl.* 1963. *(page 601)*

25-47. Andy Warhol. *Gold Marilyn Monroe.* 1962. *(page 602)*

25-48. Richard Estes. *Food Shop*. 1967. *(page 603)*

25-49. Audrey Flack. *Queen*. 1975–76. *(page 604)*

25-50. Anselm Kiefer. *To the Unknown Painter*. 1983. *(page 605)*

25-51. Elizabeth Murray. *More than You Know.*
1983. *(page 606)*

_____

_____

_____

_____

_____

_____

_____

_____

_____

_____

Chapter 26
Twentieth-Century Sculpture

Notes

26-1. Henri Matisse. *Reclining Nude I.* 1907.
(page 608)

_____

_____

_____

_____

_____

_____

_____

_____

_____

_____

26-2. Constantin Brancusi. *The Kiss.* 1909.
(page 608)

_____

_____

_____

_____

_____

_____

_____

_____

_____

26-3. Constantin Brancusi. *Bird in Space*. 1928
(unique cast). *(page 609)*

_____

_____

_____

_____

_____

_____

_____

_____

_____

_____

_____

26-4. Raymond Duchamp-Villon. *The Great
Horse*. 1914. *(page 610)*

_____

_____

_____

_____

_____

_____

_____

_____

_____

_____

_____

_____

_____

26-5. Umberto Boccioni. *Unique Forms of
Continuity in Space*. 1913 (cast 1931). *(page 610)*

_____

_____

_____

_____

_____

_____

_____

_____

_____

_____

_____

26-6. Vladimir Tatlin. *Project for Monument to the Third International.* 1919–20. *(page 611)*

_____

_____

_____

_____

_____

_____

_____

_____

_____

_____

_____

_____

26-7. Jacques Lipchitz. *Figure.* 1926–30 (cast 1937). *(page 613)*

_____

_____

_____

_____

_____

_____

_____

_____

_____

_____

_____

_____

26-8. Marcel Duchamp. *In Advance of the Broken Arm.* 1945, from the original of 1915. *(page 613)*

_____

_____

_____

_____

_____

_____

_____

_____

_____

_____

_____

26-9. Méret Oppenheim. *Object*. 1936. *(page 613)*

_____

_____

_____

_____

_____

_____

_____

_____

_____

_____

_____

26-10. Hans Arp. *Human Concretion*. 1935. *(page 614)*

_____

_____

_____

_____

_____

_____

_____

_____

_____

_____

_____

_____

26-11. Pablo Picasso. *Bull's Head*. 1943. *(page 614)*

_____

_____

_____

_____

_____

_____

_____

_____

_____

_____

_____

_____

26-12. Alexander Calder. *Lobster Trap and Fish Tail*. 1939. *(page 615)*

_____

_____

_____

_____

_____

_____

_____

_____

_____

_____

_____

26-13. Henry Moore. *Recumbent Figure*. 1938. *(page 616)*

_____

_____

_____

_____

_____

_____

_____

_____

_____

_____

26-14. Barbara Hepworth. *Sculpture with Color (Deep Blue and Red)*. 1940–42. *(page 617)*

_____

_____

_____

_____

_____

_____

_____

_____

_____

_____

_____

26-15. David Smith. Cubi series (at Bolton
Landing, New York). Stainless steel. Left: *Cubi
XVIII*. 1964. *(page 618)*

26-16. Ronald Bladen. *The X* (in the Corcoran
Gallery, Washington, D.C.). 1967. *(page 619)*

26-17. Joel Shapiro. *Untitled*. 1989–90. *(page 619)*

26-18. Martin Puryear. *The Spell*. 1985. *(page 620)*

_____

_____

_____

_____

_____

_____

_____

_____

_____

_____

_____

_____

26-19. Robert Smithson. *Spiral Jetty*. As built in 1970. *(page 621)*

_____

_____

_____

_____

_____

_____

_____

_____

_____

_____

_____

_____

26-20. Isamu Noguchi. Fountain for the John Hancock Insurance Company, New Orleans. 1961–62. *(page 622)*

_____

_____

_____

_____

_____

_____

_____

_____

_____

_____

_____

26-21. Robert Rauschenberg. *Odalisk*. 1955–58.
(page 623)

26-22. Louise Nevelson. *Black Chord*. 1964.
(page 624)

26-23. Barbara Chase-Riboud. *Confessions for Myself*. 1972. *(page 625)*

26-24. George Segal. *Cinema*. 1963. *(page 626)*

26-25. Edward Kienholz. *The State Hospital*. 1966. *(page 626)*

26-26. Joseph Kosuth. *One and Three Chairs*. 1965. *(page 627)*

26-27. Joseph Beuys. *Coyote*. Photo of performance at Rene Block Gallery, New York, 1974 *(page 628)*

_____

_____

_____

_____

_____

_____

_____

_____

_____

_____

26-28. Nam June Paik. *TV Buddha*. 1974. *(page 628)*

_____

_____

_____

_____

_____

_____

_____

_____

_____

_____

_____

Chapter 27
Twentieth-Century Architecture

Notes

27-1. Frank Lloyd Wright. Robie House,
Chicago. 1909 *(page 630)*

_____

_____

_____

_____

_____

_____

_____

_____

_____

_____

_____

27-2. Plan of the Robie House *(page 630)*

Guest room   Kitchen   Servants

Living room

Dining room   UPPER FLOOR

26-2
DRAWING
PU   Entrance hall   Boiler room   Laundry

Garage

Billiard   Children's
room   playroom   Court

LOWER FLOOR

_____

_____

_____

_____

_____

_____

_____

_____

_____

_____

27-3. Walter Gropius and Adolf Meyer. Fagus Shoe
Factory, Alfeld, Germany. 1911–14 *(page 631)*

27-4. Antonio Sant'Elia. Central Station project for
Città Nuova (after Banham). 1914 *(page 632)*

27-5. Bruno Taut. Staircase of the "Glass House,"
Werkbund Exhibition, Cologne. 1914 *(page 633)*

27-6. Max Berg. Interior of the Centennial Hall, Breslau, Germany. 1912–13 *(page 633)*

27-7. Gerrit Rietveld. Schröder House, Utrecht, the Netherlands. 1924 *(page 634)*

27-8. Walter Gropius. Shop Block, the Bauhaus, Dessau, Germany. 1925–26 *(page 635)*

27-9. Plan of the Bauhaus *(page 636)*

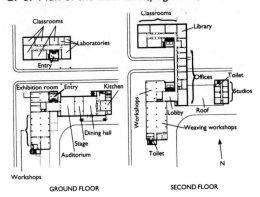

27-10. Ludwig Mies van der Rohe. German Pavilion, International Exposition, Barcelona. 1929 *(page 637)*

27-11. Le Corbusier. Villa Savoye, Poissy-sur-Seine, France. 1928–29 *(page 638)*

27-12. Alvar Aalto. Villa Mairea, Noormarkku, Finland. 1937–38 *(page 638)*

27-13. George Howe and William E. Lescaze. Philadelphia Savings Fund Society Building, Philadelphia. 1931–32 *(page 639)*

27-14. Auguste Perret. Notre Dame, Le Raincy, France. 1923–24 *(page 640)*

27-15. Ludwig Mies van der Rohe and Philip
Johnson. Seagram Building, New York.
1954–58 *(page 641)*

_____

_____

_____

_____

_____

_____

_____

_____

_____

_____

_____

27-16. Richard Rogers and Renzo Piano. Centre
National d'Art et Culture Georges Pompidou,
Paris. 1971–77 *(page 642)*

_____

_____

_____

_____

_____

_____

_____

_____

_____

_____

_____

_____

27-17. Santiago Calatrava. TGV (Train à Grande
Vitesse) Super Train Station, Satolas, Lyons.
1988–94. *(page 643)*

_____

_____

_____

_____

_____

_____

_____

_____

_____

27-18. Rem Koolhaas. Foyer of the Netherlands
Dance Theater, Amsterdam. 1987 *(page 644)*

_____

_____

_____

_____

_____

_____

_____

_____

_____

_____

_____

Chapter 28
Twentieth-Century Photography

Notes

28-1. Eugène Atget. *Pool, Versailles.* 1924.
(page 646)

_____

_____

_____

_____

_____

_____

_____

_____

_____

_____

_____

28-2. Henri Cartier-Bresson. *Mexico, 1934.*
1934. *(page 647)*

_____

_____

_____

_____

_____

_____

_____

_____

_____

_____

_____

28-3. Alfred Stieglitz. *The Steerage*. 1907.
(page 648)

_____

_____

_____

_____

_____

_____

_____

_____

_____

_____

_____

28-4. Alfred Stieglitz. *Equivalent*. 1930. *(page 649)*

_____

_____

_____

_____

_____

_____

_____

_____

_____

_____

_____

28-5. Edward Weston. *Pepper*. 1930. *(page 649)*

_____

_____

_____

_____

_____

_____

_____

_____

_____

_____

_____

_____

28-6. Ansel Adams. *Moonrise, Hernandez, New Mexico.* 1941. *(page 650)*

_____

_____

_____

_____

_____

_____

_____

_____

_____

_____

28-7. Margaret Bourke-White. *Fort Peck Dam, Montana.* 1936. *(page 651)*

_____

_____

_____

_____

_____

_____

_____

_____

_____

_____

_____

_____

28-8. James Van Der Zee. *At Home.* 1934. *(page 651)*

_____

_____

_____

_____

_____

_____

_____

_____

_____

_____

_____

28-9. August Sander. *Pastry Cook, Cologne.*
1928. *(page 652)*

_____

_____

_____

_____

_____

_____

_____

_____

_____

_____

28-10. Dorothea Lange. *Migrant Mother,*
California. 1936. *(page 653)*

_____

_____

_____

_____

_____

_____

_____

_____

_____

_____

_____

28-11. John Heartfield. *As in the Middle Ages,*
So in the Third Reich. 1934. *(page 654)*

_____

_____

_____

_____

_____

_____

_____

_____

_____

_____

28-12. Man Ray. *Untitled* (Rayograph). 1928.
(page 654)

28-13. Minor White. *Ritual Branch*. 1958. *(page 655)*

28-14. Robert Frank. *Santa Fe, New Mexico*. 1955–56. *(page 655)*

28-15. Bill Brandt. *London Child.* 1955
(page 656)

_____

_____

_____

_____

_____

_____

_____

_____

_____

_____

28-16. David Hockney. *Gregory Watching the Snow Fall, Kyoto, Feb. 21, 1983.* 1983. *(page 657)*

_____

_____

_____

_____

_____

_____

_____

_____

_____

_____

28-17. Joanne Leonard. *Romanticism Is Ultimately Fatal,* from Dreams and Nightmares series. 1982. *(page 657)*

_____

_____

_____

_____

_____

_____

_____

_____

_____

28-18. David Wojnarowicz. *Death in the Cornfield*. 1990. *(pae 658)*

_____

_____

_____

_____

_____

_____

_____

_____

_____

_____

Chapter 29
Postmodernism

Notes

29-1. Michael Graves. Public Services Building, Portland, Oregon. 1980–82 *(page 662)*

_____
_____
_____
_____
_____
_____
_____
_____
_____
_____

29-2. James Stirling, Michael Wilford and Associates. Neue Staatsgalerie, Stuttgart, Germany. Completed 1984 *(page 663)*

_____
_____
_____
_____
_____
_____
_____
_____
_____
_____
_____

29-3. Bernard Tschumi Architects. Scheme for the Pavilions, Parc de la Villette, Paris. 1982 *(page 664)*

29-4. Bernard Tschumi Architects. *Folie* P6, Parc de la Villette, Paris. 1983 *(page 664)*

29-5. Frank Gehry. Guggenheim Museum, Bilbao, Spain. 1992–97 *(page 666)*

29-6. Ilya Kabakov. *The Man Who Flew into Space from His Apartment,* from *Ten Characters.* 1981–88. *(page 668)*

29-7. Ann Hamilton. *parallel lines.* Two parts of an installation in two rooms, São Paolo Bienal, September–December 1991. *(page 669)*

29-8. Pepón Osorio. *Badge of Honor.* 1995. *(page 670)*

29-9. A. R. Penck. *The Demon of Curiosity.*
1982. *(page 671)*

_____

_____

_____

_____

_____

_____

_____

_____

_____

_____

_____

_____

29-10. Mark Tansey. Derrida Queries de Man.
1990. *(page 672)*

_____

_____

_____

_____

_____

_____

_____

_____

_____

_____

_____

_____

_____

29-11. Barbara Kruger. *You Are a Captive
Audience.* 1983. *(page 673)*

_____

_____

_____

_____

_____

_____

_____

_____

_____

_____

_____

_____